How do you make a Skeleton laugh?

Other books in this series:

**What Wears a Sock
on its Bottom?**

**What Happens When
the Queen Burps?**

**What Do You Call a
One-eyed Dinosaur?**

Poetry Collections by John Foster:

School's Out

Excuses, Excuses

Football Fever

I've Got a Poem For You

Poetry by John Foster:

The Poetry Chest

How do you make a Skeleton laugh?

Rib-tickling jokes, riddles, and rhymes selected by John Foster

Illustrated by Mark Oliver

OXFORD
UNIVERSITY PRESS

OXFORD

UNIVERSITY PRESS

Great Clarendon Street, Oxford OX2 6DP

Oxford University Press is a department of the University of Oxford.
It furthers the University's objective of excellence in research, scholarship,
and education by publishing worldwide in

Oxford New York

Auckland Cape Town Dar es Salaam Hong Kong Karachi
Kuala Lumpur Madrid Melbourne Mexico City Nairobi
New Delhi Shanghai Taipei Toronto

With offices in

Argentina Austria Brazil Chile Czech Republic France Greece
Guatemala Hungary Italy Japan Poland Portugal Singapore
South Korea Switzerland Thailand Turkey Ukraine Vietnam

Oxford is a registered trade mark of Oxford University Press
in the UK and in certain other countries

British Library Cataloguing in Publication Data
Data available

ISBN: 978-0-19-275739-5
1 3 5 7 9 10 8 6 4 2

Printed in Great Britain
Paper used in the production of this book is a natural,
recyclable product made from wood grown in sustainable forests.
The manufacturing process conforms to the environmental
regulations of the country of origin.

CONTENTS

FUNNY BONES AND SPARE RIBS

How do you make a skeleton laugh?
By tickling its funny bone.

Why did the skeleton go to the Chinese takeaway?
To get some spare ribs.

What did the skeleton say to his friend in a storm?
'Oooh that wind goes straight through me.'

Why did Old Mother Hubbard shriek?
Because she found a skeleton in the cupboard.

What do you call a lazy skeleton?
Bone idle.

What did the vulture say to the skeleton?
I've a bone to pick with you.

Why are skeletons so calm?
Nothing gets under their skin.

Why are skeletons always lonely?
They haven't got any body to keep them company.

Why wouldn't the skeleton cross the road?
He didn't have the guts.

What is a skeleton's favourite instrument?
The trom-bone.

The Magician's Ghost
The ghost of the magician
Said, 'I'm really in a fix.
The trouble is the audience
See right through all my tricks.'

A Skeleton Once in Khartoum
A skeleton once in Khartoum
Discovered a ghost in his room;
They spent the whole night
Shivering with fright
Wondering who should be
frightened of whom.

WHICH WITCH?

What does a witch ask for when she's staying
in a hotel?
Broom service.

What did the skeleton say to the twin witches?
Which witch is which?

What was the name of the witch's father?
He was cauldron.

How do you make a witch scratch?
Drop the w to make her itch.

What do you call a nervous witch?
Twitch.

The Wizard of Oz
The wonderful wizard of Oz
Retired from the business because
What with up-to-date science,
To most of his clients
He wasn't the wizard he was.

Wanda's Academy for Witches
School Report for B. Wicked   *Hallowe'en Term*

Transformation: Needs to concentrate more. Keeps turning herself into a hyena and won't stop cackling.

Witchcraft: Her spell-weaving is improving.

Flying: Must control her temper. Sometimes loses control of her broomstick and flies off the handle.

Appearance: Very good. Has developed some revolting warts and is growing uglier every term.

Hygiene: Excellent. Has managed not to wash all term and is developing a pungent odour.

Behaviour: Is making progress at being consistently bad.

Overall: Is beginning to become an enchanting person.

ROLLER GHOSTERS AND HIDE AND SHRIEK

Which ride do ghosts like best at the theme park?
The roller ghoster.

Why did the ghost stop buying lottery tickets?
Because he didn't have a ghost of a chance of winning.

What is a ghost's favourite game?
Hide and shriek.

Where do baby ghosts go when their parents
are out haunting?
Dayscare.

What is a ghost's favourite form of transport?
Scare-o-plane.

What does the headless horseman ride?
A night-mare.

Where do ghosts go swimming?
In the Dead Sea.

Boo!

There Once was a Ghost Called Paul
There once was a ghost called Paul
Who went to a fancy dress ball.
To shock all the guests
He went quite undressed
But no one could see him at all.

What did the ghost teacher say to the class?
Watch the board and I'll go through it again.

When do ghosts play tricks on each other?
April Ghoul's Day.

What are a ghost's favourite foods?
Dreaded wheat and ghoulash.

Where will you never find a ghost in a haunted house?
The living room.

I KNOW A GIRL CALLED NORAH BONE

I know a girl called Norah Bone.
She's got a friend called Mona Lotte.

That's nothing.

I know a boy called Neil Down.
He's got a friend called Stan Duppe.

That's nothing.

I know a boy called Ivor Screwloose.
He's got a friend called Lou Chain.

That's nothing.

I know a boy called Ben Nevis.
He's got a friend called Rocky Mountain.

That's nothing.

I know a boy called Dicky Bird.
He's got a friend called Polly Parrot.

That's nothing.

I know a boy called Jim Shoe.
He's got a friend called Bobbie Socks.

That's nothing.

I know a girl called Hazel Nutt.
She's got a friend called Marguerita Pizza.

People Who Lived Up to Their Names

Justin Amin was never ready on time.
Percival Pickalock led a life of crime.
Bert Balderdash talked a lot of
nonsense.
Hatty Hesitate always sat on the fence.
Walter Wrigglebum would never sit still.
Stanley Sickalot was always ill.
Imogen Idle was utterly lazy.
Cyril Crackers was completely crazy.
Norman Nailbiter suffered from stress.
Charlotte Carefree couldn't care less.

Name the Girl, Name the Boy—A Word Puzzle

1. Which girl can be found in a yacht?
2. Which boy can be found in a cigar?
3. Which girl can be found hiding in a habitat?
4. Which boy can be found turning round a warden?
5. Which girl can be found in a breath?
6. Which girl is found with a different label?
7. Which boy can be seen wandering yonder?
8. Which boy is in denial?
9. Which girl can be found in dangle?
10. Which boy is tangled up in a spire?

CRAZY COPS AND RIDICULOUS ROBBERS

Why did the belt go to jail?
Because it held up some trousers.

Newsflash
Two dozen computer screens were stolen from a van last night. Police are said to be monitoring the situation.

Who was the world's greatest thief?
Atlas, because he held up the whole world.

There Once Was a Man Called Finnigan
There once was a man called Finnigan
Who broke out of jail to sin again.
He broke laws by the dozen
Even stole from his cousin
Now the jail he broke out of, he's in again.

Why was the photographer arrested?
*The police found his prints at the scene
of the crime.*

Break-In News
A lorryload of filing cabinets and documents was
stolen last night. Police think there might be links
to organized crime.

Newsflash
A set of traffic lights has been stolen from a main
road junction in Reading. A police spokesman said,
'Some thieves will stop at nothing.'

Why was the policeman carrying a pencil
and a thin piece of paper?
Because he wanted to trace someone.

A woman has been found dead in a bathtub full of milk and cornflakes. Police are looking for a cereal killer.

Why did Robin Hood only rob the rich?
Because the poor didn't have anything worth stealing.

A woman woke her husband in the middle of the night. 'There's a burglar downstairs eating the cake I made yesterday.'
'Who shall I call,' her husband said, 'police or ambulance?'

SNAKE BITES AND RATSNATCHERS

What do you call a
snake that is a police
informer?
A grass-snake.

What do snakes do after a fight?
They hiss and make up.

What do you get if you cross
two snakes with a magic spell?
Addercadabra and abradacobra.

In which river are you
bound to find snakes?
The Hiss-issippi.

In what school subject do
snakes always get A grades?
Hiss-tory.

What is a snake's
favourite game?
Snakes and Ladders.

Why didn't the viper
viper her nose?
Because the adder adder handkerchief.

What's long and green and goes hith?
A snake with a lisp.

What do you call a snake that
works for the government?
A civil serpent.

Why couldn't the
snake talk?
*Because he had a
frog in his throat.*

Snake 1: Are we poisonous?
Snake 2: *I don't know. Why?*
Snake 1: I just bit my lip.

19

Get Ratty

What do you call a well-bred rat?
An aristo-rat.

What do you call a young rat that is behaving badly?
A brat.

What is a baby rat's favourite toy?
A rattle.

How do rats offer their thanks?
They show gratitude.

What do you call a bad-tempered rat?
Ratty.

What is a rat's favourite nursery rhyme?
Jack Sprat.

What does a rat say when it breaks something?
Drat!

What do you call a rat from Transylvania?
A vampire rat.

What is a rat's favourite food?
Ratatouille.

DEAD FUNNY

Epitaph for an Auctioneer
Going, going, GONE!

Epitaph for a Dentist
Stranger, approach this spot with gravity,
John Brown is filling his last cavity.

Epitaph for a Football Referee
Here lies the body of Percy Thistle,
A ref who has blown his final whistle.

Epitaph for a Cleaner
Here lies a cleaner Betty Broom.
Now she sweeps inside this tomb.

Stephen Crotchet, Musician
Stephen and time are now both even,
Stephen beat time, now time's beat Stephen.

John Mill
Here lies a liar, John Mill,
Who maintained he wasn't ill.
He lied. He died.
He's lying still.

Undertakers—Your Questions Answered

Do undertakers enjoy their work?
Of corpse they do.

How do undertakers speak?
Gravely.

Who wrote 'A *Guide to Undertaking*'?
Paul Bearer.

How do undertakers fasten their ties?
With wreath knots.

Notice in a Cemetery

Persons are prohibited from picking flowers
from any but their own graves.

Here Lies a Robot

Here lies a robot.
Deprived of grease,
He ceased to work.
May he rust in peace.

Charlotte Cul-de-Sac

Here lies Charlotte Cul-de-Sac,
A most annoying friend,
She used to drive me round the bend,
Until she came to a dead end.

YOU HAVE BEEN WARNED!

A Cheeky Boy Called Robert Rung—a cautionary tale

A cheeky boy called Robert Rung
Was always sticking out his tongue
At everybody that he saw
Passing by the village store.
Till one day he went too far.
A driver, leaping from his car,
Shouted out, 'You little toad!'
And chased young Robert down the road
Into a farmyard nearby,
Where Robert slipped and, with a cry,
Fell headlong in a steaming pile
Of manure, squelchy and vile,
So that cheeky Robert Rung
Was covered head to foot in dung.
Which is why when you are young
You never should stick out your tongue.

Ernie—A Cautionary Tale

Ernie watched so much TV
He put down roots in the settee.
At night he never went to bed.
He vegetated there instead.

He stared and stared, hour after hour.
His face became a pale white flower.
Green leaves sprouted from his hair.
He drove his parents to despair.

His mother fetched a watering can.
'You'll never grow into a man,'
She sighed and, sprinkling him with care,
She pulled some weeds out of his hair.

Sandra Slater

Here lies what's left of Sandra Slater
Who poked her pet—an alligator—
Forgetting that to tease or bait her
Might annoy an alligator.
Alas, the alligator ate her.

Never Throw a Brick at a Drowning Man
Never throw a brick at a drowning man
Or a lifebelt made of straw
Always throw him a bar of soap
So he'll wash himself ashore.

Warning! A List of Things Not To Do
Don't be superstitious—it's bad luck.

Never test the depth of the water with both feet.

Never walk under a cow—you risk getting a pat
  on the head.

Don't comment on Auntie Mabel's moustache.

Don't wait until you've been to the toilet to
  check whether there's any paper.

If your dad's angry and says 'Do you think
  I'm stupid?' don't answer.

Never, never, never, never repeat.

BATTY BOOKS AND POTTY PLAYS

A Solitary Life by I. Malone.

Body Odours by U. Stink.

Vegetarian Breakfasts by Egbert Nobacon.

Electrical Faults by Lou Swires.

The Haunted House by Hugo First.

Football Champions by R. Senal.

How to Catch Worms by Earl E. Bird.

Feeling Sick by Henrietta Maggot.

The London Underground by Victoria Line.

The End of School by Wendy Bellgoes.

Bullying Hurts by Howard U. Likeit.

An Extra Week's Holiday by Trudi Light.

Telling Fibs by Eliza Lott.

Keeping the Garden Tidy by Moses Lawn.

Is That a Yes or a No? by May Bee.

Ten Shakespeare Plays You Won't Have Seen

Omelette, Prince of Denmark

A Midsummer Night's Scream

Mockbreath

Thirteenth Night

Julius Frees Her

Much Ado About Everything

The Meerkat of Venice

Alfa Romeo and Juliet

ANT, DEC AND CLEOPATRA

A Comedy of Terrors

WHAT'S THE DIFFERENCE? AND LIKE FOR LIKE

What's the difference?
What's the difference between unlawful and illegal?
Unlawful is against the law and illegal is a sick bird.

What's the difference between a buffalo
and a bison?
Have you ever tried to wash your hands in a buffalo?

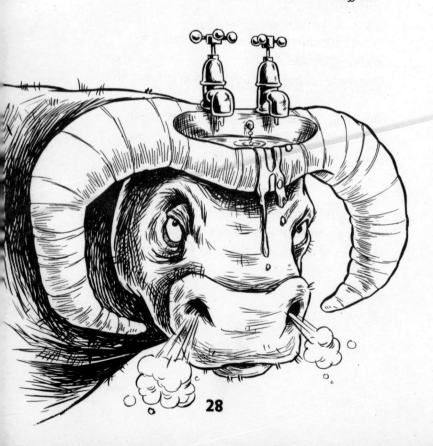

What's the difference between a big black
cloud and a lion with toothache?
One pours with rain and the other roars with pain.

What's the difference between an angry
rabbit and a forged £5 note?
One is a mad bunny and the other is bad money.

What's the difference between a flea and a wolf?
*One prowls on the hairy and one howls on
the prairie.*

What's the difference between an oak tree
and a tight shoe?
One makes acorns, the other makes corns ache.

What's the difference between a square peg
in a round hole and a kilo of lard?
*One's a fat lot of good and the other's a good
lot of fat.*

What's the difference between a flea-bitten
dog and someone who needs the toilet?
One's going to itch and the other's itching to go.

What's the difference between a church bell and a thief?
One peals from the steeple and the other steals from the people.

Like For Like
Why is a chicken like a guitar?
Because both can be plucked.

Why is a sofa like a roast turkey?
Because both are full of stuffing.

When is a shoe like a very hot dog?
When its tongue is hanging out.

Why is a coin like a cat?
Because both of them have heads and tails.

Why is an onion like a bell?
Because both can be peeled.

Why are goldfish like breakfast cereals?
Because they both come in bowls.

Why are vampires like false teeth?
Because they both come out at night.

TOMBSTONE TART AND EYES SCREAM

Where do vampires go on holiday?
The Isle of Fright.

What is Dracula's favourite sport?
Casketball.

What song do vampires sing on New Year's Eve?
Auld Fang Syne.

How do vampires sail across the sea?
In blood vessels.

What are twin vampires called?
Blood brothers.

What did Count Dracula get from biting a snowman?
Frost bite.

Does Dracula like to take a shower after a night out?
He prefers a blood bath.

What did Dracula say to his girlfiend?
It was love at first bite.

What did the mother vampire say to her son
at dinner-time?
Hurry up and drink your soup before it clots.

Why was Dracula sad?
His love was in vein.

What did the boy vampire say to the glamorous
girl vampire?
Hello, gore-juice.

Why doesn't the young vampire have
any friends at school?
Because he's a pain in the neck.

DINE AT DRACULA'S
The Coffin Restaurant,
666 Undertakers Lane, Deadbury

First Corpse
Scream of skeleton soup

Dreaded shark bites

Maggots on toast

Main Corpse
Roast snake with lady's fingers

Ghoulash

Mummified meatballs with cauliflower ears

Spare ribs (suitable for skeletons)

Spagyeti with grated knees

Scotch legs with toenail salad

Desserts
Eyes scream

Tombstone tart

Necktarines

Full range of Transylvanian red wines,
Crematorium biers and Slime juices.

10% discount for funeral parties

You Can Count On Me

'You can count on me,' said the Count,
Sharpening his teeth with a file.
He leant over the blood donor
And gave him a wicked smile.

'It will all be over in a flash.
All you will feel is a little nip.'
The Count smacked his lips together,
Then bent down and started to sip.

The Count took a long drink, then said,
'Here's a plaster to put on the bite.'
Wiping his chin, he gave a huge grin,
'See you in the crypt later tonight!'

CRAZY CAROLS AND CHRISTMAS CRACKERS

As Shepherds Watched Their Flocks

As shepherds watched their flocks by night
While tuned to BBC,
The angel of the Lord came down
And switched to ITV.

Hark, the Herald Angels Sing

Hark, the herald angels sing,
What will Father Christmas bring?
New false teeth for Grandpa John,
A new toupee for Uncle Ron,
Fresh breath mints for Aunty Fanny,
Anti-wrinkle cream for Granny,
Dieting books for Aunty Pru,
Spot cream for my sister Sue.
Hark, the herald angels sing,
What will Father Christmas bring?

Christmas Crackers

What do you call a deer with no eyes?
No idea.

What did one eye say to the other eye?
Between you and me something smells.

What flowers grow on your face?
Two-lips.

What do you call a fortunate detective?
Sheerluck Holmes.

What is a frog's favourite flower?
A croak-us.

Why was the broom late?
Because it overswept.

Why was the rubbish sad?
Because it was down in the dumps.

Why did the girl put lipstick on her forehead?
Because she was trying to make up her mind.

Why was the calendar so anxious?
Because its days were numbered.

What does a magician keep up his sleeve?
His arm.

What's got a bottom at the top?
A toilet.

Why do idiots eat biscuits?
Because they are crackers.

What clothes does a house wear?
Address.

What is round, white and giggles?
A tickled onion.

LUDICROUS LIMERICKS

I Sat Next to the Duchess at Tea

I sat next to the duchess at tea.
It was just as I feared it would be.
Her rumblings abdominal
Were simply phenomenal
And everyone thought it was me!

There Was an Old Man of Blackheath

There was an old man of Blackheath
Who sat on his set of false teeth,
Said he with a start,
'Oh Lord bless my heart!
I have bitten myself underneath!'

There Was a Young Lady From Ickenham

There was a young lady from Ickenham
Who went on a bus trip to Twickenham.
She drank too much beer
Which made her feel queer
So she took off her boots and was sick in 'em.

A Dentist Named Archibald Moss

A dentist named Archibald Moss
Fell in love with the dainty Miss Ross.
Since he held in abhorrence
Her Christian name Florence,
He renamed her his dear dental Floss.

There Was a Young Woman Called Grace

There was a young woman called Grace
Whose nose spread all over her face.
She got very few kisses
And the reason for this is
There wasn't a suitable place.

A French Poodle
A French poodle espied in the hall
A pool a wet brolly let fall.
He said, 'Ah oui oui!
This time it's not me,
But I'm bound to be blamed for it all.'

DOTTY DEFINITIONS

archive: where Noah kept his bees.
blazer: a jacket that is on fire.
calendar: something that goes in one year
and out the other.
denial: a river which runs through Egypt.
dynamite: a flea having a meal in a restaurant.
eclipse: what a gardener does to a hedge.
faith: what you thee when you look in a mirror.
gargoyle: what you do when you have a
sore throat.
intent: determined to go camping.
ketchup: to draw level with the others in a race.
melancholy: a sad sheepdog.
out of bounds: an exhausted kangaroo.
posse: a wild west cat.

quicksand: sand blown across the desert during a sandstorm.
selfish: what a fishmonger does.
tax: nails which workers have to pay the government.
zeal: an enthusiastic sea creature.

MAJOR ANSWER

Knock, knock.
Who's there?
Major.
Major who?
Major answer, didn't I?

Knock, knock.
Who's there?
Howard.
Howard who?
Howard you know if you won't even open the door?

Knock, knock.
Who's there?
Lettuce.
Lettuce who?
Lettuce in. I've forgotten my key.

Knock, knock.
Who's there?
Luke.
Luke who?
Luke through the letter box and see for yourself.

Knock, knock.
Who's there?
Rice Krispies.
Rice Krispies who?
I'll tell you next week. It's a serial.

Knock, knock.
Who's there?
Earwig.
Earwig who?
Earwig go! Earwig go! Earwig go!

Knock, knock.
Who's there?
Justin.
Justin who?
Justin time. I was about to go away.

Knock, knock.
Who's there?
Amos.
Amos who?
A mosquito.

Knock, knock.
Who's there?
Juicy.
Juicy who?
Jui see me? I can see you!

Knock, knock.
Who's there?
Bella.
Bella who?
Bella not working. That's why I knock.

TELL THEM TO BUZZ OFF

Who's That at the Door?
Someone selling a sat nav.
Tell them to get lost.

Someone with a drum.
Tell them to beat it.

A kangaroo.
Tell him to hop it.

A swarm of bees.
Tell them to buzz off.

Someone selling children's scooters.
Tell them to push off.

Someone selling freezers.
Give him the cold shoulder.

Someone wanting you to join an athletics club.
Tell them to take a running jump.

Someone selling barometers.
Tell them you'll take a raincheck.

DOCTOR, DOCTOR, I FEEL LIKE A PACK OF CARDS

Doctor, doctor, I think I've got amnesia.
Go home and forget about it.

Doctor, doctor, I feel like a window.
Where's the pane?

Doctor, doctor, I keeping seeing an insect
walking around in circles.
Don't worry, it's just a bug that's going round.

Newsflash
Poison Victim Expected To Make Full Recovery
Ethel Gardener (68) who poisoned herself by eating
a daffodil bulb is expected to make a full recovery.
A doctor who is treating her at Potters Bar hospital
said she would be out in the spring.

Doctor, doctor, I feel like a bell.
Take these and, if they don't work, give me a ring.

Doctor, doctor, everyone keeps ignoring me.
Next, please.

Doctor, doctor, I keep seeing images of
Donald Duck and Mickey Mouse
When did these Disney spells start?

Doctor, doctor, I feel like a pack of cards.
Stop shuffling. I'll deal with you later.

Doctor, doctor, I feel like an apple.
We must get to the core of this.

Doctor, doctor, I think I'm Napoleon.
How long has this been going on?
Ever since Waterloo.

Doctor, doctor, I keep thinking I'm a clock.
Try not to get so wound up.

Angry patient: I can't have an appointment with the doctor in a month! I could be dead by then.
Receptionist: If you are, please ask your wife to cancel it.

Why did the nurse tiptoe past the medicine cabinet?
She didn't want to wake the sleeping tablets.

Doctor, doctor, I can't stop trembling.
I'll be with you in two shakes.

Doctor, doctor, I keep thinking I'm a bridge.
What's come over you?
Six lorries, four cars, and a motorcycle.

FOOTBALL FUNNIES

The Goalkeeper from Tibet
A young goalkeeper from Tibet
Made an error he'll never forget.
He missed a back pass,
'Cause he slipped on the grass
And the ball trickled into the net.

When the Moon Turns Green
When the moon turns green and the sun is blue
And sausages dance down the hill,
Luton Town will win the cup,
But Carlisle never will.

Final Scores
Wolves 6 Sheep 0
Hearts 1 Lungs 2
Spurs 2 Stirrups 2
Queen's Park 1 King's Cross 0
West Ham 2 Easter Eggs 4
Chesterfield 4 Divan 0
Thistle 1 Nettles 1
Blackpool 0 Whirlpool 0
Crewe 2 Passengers 0
Bury 1 Gravesend 1

Fantasy Football

From the **HARDTOWN UNITED** website

Club **Hardtown United**   *Ground* **The Mayhem**

Club motto **By foul means**

Manager **M. Winatallcosts** *Coach* **B. Vicious**

Nickname **The Bovver Boys**

Fanzine **The Hardmen**

Cup Winning Team

Vinnie Violent

Gert Trippemup   Eimer Crunchintackler

Billy Bodychecker   Ivor Puttisbootin

Willie Breaker-Legg

Chop Yu Down   I. Foulalot (Capt.)

El Bo Inface

Will Pulyershirt

Eimer Shinkicker

Substitutes

R. U. Hardenough

Y. B. Hurt-Letuswin

E. Will Maimem

E. B. A. Maniac

Ed Butter

IRISH SPEW AND BOGEY PIE

School Dinners

What's for dinner? What's for dinner?
Irish spew, Irish spew,
Sloppy semolina, sloppy semolina,
No thank you, no thank you.

Splishy splashy custard, dead dogs' eyes,
All mixed up with giblet pies,
Spread it on the butty nice and thick,
Swallow it down with a bucket of sick.

Hotch scotch, bogey pie,
Mix it up with a dead man's eye,
Earthworm soup, hard-boiled snails,
Manure on toast with fried rat's tails.

An Epicure Dining at Crewe

An epicure dining at Crewe
Found quite a large mouse in his stew;
Said the waiter, 'Don't shout
Or wave it about,
Or the rest will be wanting one too!'

Diddle, Diddle, Dumpling

Diddle, diddle dumpling, my son John
Ate a pasty five feet long;
He bit it once, he bit it twice.
Oh, my goodness, it was full of mice!

Captain Cook

Captain Cook made some soup.
His mother made some jelly.
Captain Cook's soup was so hot that
He burnt a hole in his belly.

Knock, knock
'Who's there?'
'Arthur.'
'Arthur who?'
'Arthur any more biscuits? I'm still hungry.'

Waiter, waiter, how long will my sausages be?
About three inches.

Waiter, waiter, will my pizza be long?
No, sir, round.

Waiter, waiter, this coffee tastes like mud.
Well, sir, it was ground yesterday.

Waiter, waiter, there's a button in my lettuce.
Oh, that must be from the salad dressing.

Waiter, waiter, there's a worm on my plate.
That's not a worm, sir, that's your sausage.

Waiter, waiter, there's a dead beetle in my soup.
Yes, sir, they're not very good swimmers.

Waiter, waiter, bring me something to eat and make it snappy.
How about a crocodile sandwich, sir.

SIX SICK SIKHS MET SIX SICK SHEIKS

Tongue Twisters

Sue Shore Shrieked
Sue Shore shrieked.
Sue Shore shouted, 'Shoo!'
Sue was sure she saw
A shrew in her shoe.

Six Sick Sikhs Met Six Sick Sheiks
Six sick Sikhs met six sick sheiks.
'Shake hands,' said the Sikhs.
'Shake hands,' said the sheiks.
'We're sick of being sick,'
said the six sick Sikhs.
'We're sick of being sick,'
said the six sick sheiks.
Six Sikhs with the shivers.
Six sheiks with the shakes.

Underwood's Underwear
Underwood would wear underwear
If Underwood knew where
Underwood put
Underwood's underwear.

Nicola Nicholas

Nicola Nicholas couldn't care less.
Nicola Nicholas tore her dress.
Nicola Nicholas tore her knickers.
Now Nicola Nicholas is knickerless.

Shaun Short's Short Shorts

Shaun Short bought some shorts.
The shorts were shorter than Shaun Short thought.
Shaun Short's short shorts were so short,
Shaun Short thought, Shaun you ought
Not to have bought shorts so short.

DON'T OPEN THE DOOR
TO A DINOSAUR

Advice to Travellers

Don't take a chance
In France
If a mermaid asks you to dance.

In Crete
If you meet King Kong in the street
Don't mention his smelly feet.

In Bangalore
Don't open the door
To a dinosaur.

Whatever you do,
Don't sail to Peru
In a boat with a skeleton crew.

Holiday Hints

Lovers might go to Darlington
And plumbers might go to Leek,
And radio presenters
Should feel at home in Speke.

Bachelors might go to Singleton,
While sailors go to Crewe.
Pilots might go to Ayr
And gardeners to Kew.

Undertakers might go to Bury,
Librarians to Great Bookham,
Fire officers to Burntwood
And caterers to Cookham.

Bookmakers might go to Gamblestown,
Weather forecasters to Hale,
Foresters to Woodland
And auctioneers to Sale.

WHERE DO FISH KEEP
THEIR MONEY?

Dinner Date
'Twas in a restaurant they met,
Romeo and Juliet.
He had no cash to pay the debt,
So Romeo'd while Juliet.

Why did the baker work so hard?
Because he kneaded the dough.

Where do fish keep their money?
In river banks.

Why are fleas always short of money?
Because they scratch out a living.

How do you stop a buffalo from charging?
You take away its credit card.

When does it rain money?
When there's a change in the weather.

What's the quickest way to double your money?
Fold it in half.

What do you call someone who is crazy
about money?
A doughnut.

What do misers do when it's cold?
Sit round a candle.

What do misers do when it's really cold?
Light it.

Why did the gold prospector quit his job?
Things just didn't pan out.

What would happen if money grew on trees?
There wouldn't be much shade.

I WISH I WERE A DOZEN EGGS

I Wish I Were a Dozen Eggs

I wish I were a dozen eggs
Sitting in a tree
And when you passed along below
I'd splatter you with me.

As I Was Going Out One Day

As I was going out one day,
My head fell off and rolled away.
But when I saw that it was gone,
I picked it up and put it on.
And when I got into the street,
A fellow cried: 'Look at your feet!'
I looked at them and sadly said:
'I've left them both asleep in bed!'

What's Your Name?

What's your name?
Tobias Toad.
Where do you live?
Rhubarb Road.
What's your job?
Counting sheep.
Where do you work?
Where people can't sleep.

What's your name?
Norah Neate.
Where do you live?
Sausage Street.
What's your job?
Tying knots.
Where do you work?
Beauty spots.

What's your name?
Betty Brain.
Where do you live?
Lettuce Lane.
What's your job?
Splitting hairs.
Where do you work?
Under the stairs.

What's your name?
Sebastien Snare.
Where do you live?
Shortbread Square.
What's your job?
Cutting corners.
Where do you live?
Little Jack Horner's.

Mr Wister's Sister
Mr Wister had a sister,
Who was so tall, no one had kissed her.
So a certain Mr Adder
Went and fetched a builder's ladder.

Toot! Toot!

A peanut sat on a railway track,
His heart was all a-flutter;
The five-fifteen came rushing by—
Toot! Toot! He's peanut butter!

WHY DID THE LOBSTER BLUSH?

Why is the sea restless?
Because it has stones in its bed.

Why did the lobster blush?
Because the sea weed.

Why won't prawns share their sweets?
Because they're shelfish.

A Sea-Serpent Saw a Big Tanker

A sea-serpent saw a big tanker,
Bit a hole in her side and then sank her.
It swallowed the crew
In a minute or two
And then picked its teeth with the anchor.

A Bug and a Flea

A bug and a flea
Went to sea
On a reel of cotton.
The bug was drowned.
The flea was found
Stuck to a mermaid's bottom.

Fishy Questions

What's the best way to communicate with a fish?
Drop them a line.

Who do fish go to when they need to borrow money?
A loan shark.

Who held the baby octopus to ransom?
Squidnappers.

What did the fish say to his friend in the aquarium?
Long time, no sea.

Seaside Riddles

1. Spend a day at the seaside and you'll see
   How hard it can be to get rid of me.
   You carry me home as you walk down the street
   In between toes, on the soles of your feet.
   Then when you get home and open the door,
   I sprinkle myself all over the floor.
   I'm fun to play with, but, as you can see,
   You'll need a Hoover to get rid of me.

2. I stand on stilts. You can walk on me,
   Out from the land, above the sea.

3. When I'm in, I am high.
   When I'm out, I am low.
   To find me you need
   To go with the flow.

4. I beam at passers-by
   A warning loud and clear
   Of dangers that lurk beneath
   If they stray too near.

5. I am a fortress for today.
   Tomorrow I'll be wiped away.

6. A strong wind is what I need
   To skim across the bay at speed.
   I've only one wing, but watch me fly
   Over the waves as I race by.

7. Drop me and my iron claw
   Will hold you steady by the shore.
   Haul me up and you will be
   Ready again to go to sea.

8. I scuttle and claw across the sand.
   Don't touch me or I'll nip your hand.

9. Topped with foam, sometimes we roar
   Or else we calmly stroke the shore.

10. Smiling, I sit upon the rocks
    Combing my soft and golden locks,
    Enchanting sailors who always fail
    To see my shining, silver tail.

MONDAY'S CHILD IS AS SLIMY AS A SNAIL

Yankee Doodle Came to Town

Yankee Doodle came to town
Riding on a poodle
He stuck a banana in each ear
And called it chicken noodle.

Monday's Child Is As Slimy As a Snail

Monday's child is as slimy as a snail
Tuesday's child has a long forked tail
Wednesday's child has slavering jaws
Thursday's child has razor-sharp claws
Friday's child snarls and howls
Saturday's child lurks and prowls
And the child that is born on Sunday night
Has talons that scratch and fangs that bite!

Ride a Sock-horse

Ride a sock-horse to Aston Villa
To see a fine lady ride on a gorilla.
With pearls in her ears and snow on her toes
She shall bring moonshine wherever she goes.

Mary, Mary

Mary, Mary, quite contrary
Texting to her friends,
Walked into a lamp-post
And there her message ends.

Nursery Rhyme Storytapes

Off to the Market by Tobias A. Pig.

Why I Avoid Fatty Foods by Jack Sprat.

The Empty Cupboard by M. Hubbard.

The Cat Down the Well by Johnny
    Green and Johnny Stout.

A Rainy Day in Gloucester by Doctor Foster.

Banbury Cross by Rhoda Whitehorse.

Candlestick Jumping by Jack B. Nimble.

How We Tried to Save Humpty Dumpty
   by A. Kingsman.

Marching Up and Down by the Duke of York.

Sat in the Corner by L. J. Horner.

Three Mice Tails by A. Farmer-Swife.

THOUGHT FOR THE DAY

If you jogged backwards, would you gain weight?

A wise man never plays leapfrog with a unicorn.

Those who like ironing find their pleasure
in creases.

When the wheel was invented it caused a
revolution.

What goes around usually gets dizzy and falls over.

A stitch in time means you have run far enough.

It's a fact: taller people sleep longer in bed.

Exit signs are on the way out.

CRAZY CONVERSATIONS

What did the barman say to the ghost who
tried to order a drink?
I'm sorry, we don't serve spirits.

What did one pair of glasses say to another
pair of glasses?
Stop making a spectacle of yourself.

What did the mother ghost say to her children?
Put your boos and shocks on.

What did the ground say to the earthquake?
You crack me up.

What did the tie say to the hat?
You go on ahead and I'll hang around.

What did the traffic light say to the car?
Don't look. I'm changing.

What did the picture say to the wall?
I've got you covered.

THE INVISIBLE MAN SAID...

1. It's no good, we'll never see eye to eye.

2. Look at me, when I'm talking to you.

3. Why does everyone keep ignoring me?

4. Don't push in front of me. I was here before you.

5. Do you mind not sitting on my lap? Can't you see this seat's taken.

6. If you can't see me, who are you talking to?

7. My friends call me Window, because they can see right through me.

8. I don't know why I bother. No one takes any notice of me.

TEACHER, TEACHER

God Made the Bees
God made the bees.
The bees make the honey.
We do all the work.
The teachers make the money.

Teacher's Strong
Teacher's strong;
Teacher's gentle.
Teacher's kind
And I am mental.

Notice outside the school caretaker's room

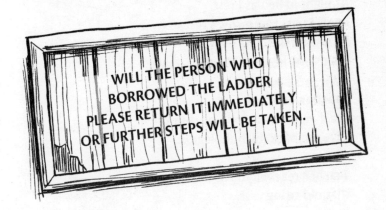

WILL THE PERSON WHO
BORROWED THE LADDER
PLEASE RETURN IT IMMEDIATELY
OR FURTHER STEPS WILL BE TAKEN.

The Night Before the Test
At night in bed as I rest,
I pray I pass tomorrow's test.
If I should die before I wake
That's one less test I'll have to take.

Teacher, Teacher
Teacher, teacher, don't be dumb,
Give me back my bubblegum.

Teacher, teacher you're the best when you wear
that old string vest.

Teacher, teacher, I declare,
Tarzan's lost his underwear.

Teacher, teacher come here quick Stella Brown has
just been sick.

Teacher, teacher, don't be mean,
Give me some money for the Coke machine.

Teacher, teacher no more school, let's go down to
the swimming pool.

School Reports (for a class in which everyone is called Ann)

Ann Gelic	*Always well-behaved.*
Ann Ger	*Needs to learn to control her temper.*
Ann Ecdote	*Excels at storytelling.*
Ann Tagonist	*Can sometimes act in a hostile manner.*
Ann Ticipate	*Always well-prepared.*
Ann Thology	*Has read a wide collection of stories and poems.*
Ann Tic	*Frequently behaves in a silly way.*
Ann Iversary	*Good at remembering key dates.*
Ann Agram	*Has a habit of changing letters around when she writes.*
Ann Ouncer	*Has a good knowledge of current affairs and is a good communicator.*
Ann Oying	*Tends to be very irritating.*
Ann Them	*Sings loudly and patriotically.*

SENSELESS SIGNS

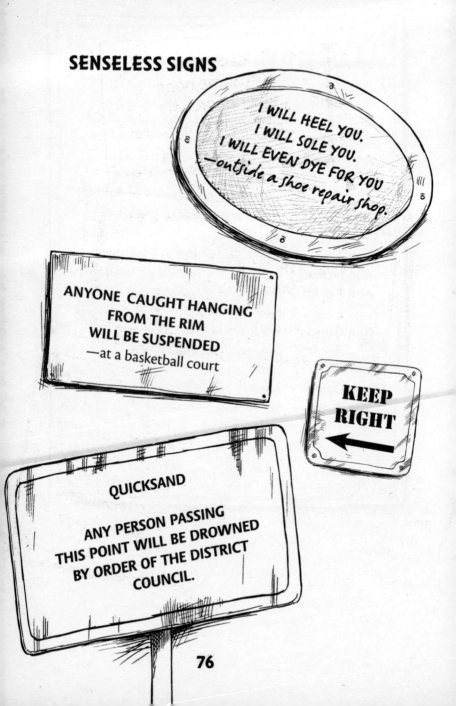

I WILL HEEL YOU.
I WILL SOLE YOU.
I WILL EVEN DYE FOR YOU
—outside a shoe repair shop.

ANYONE CAUGHT HANGING
FROM THE RIM
WILL BE SUSPENDED
—at a basketball court

KEEP RIGHT

QUICKSAND

ANY PERSON PASSING
THIS POINT WILL BE DROWNED
BY ORDER OF THE DISTRICT
COUNCIL.

CAUTION:
AUTOMATIC DOOR
PUSH TO OPERATE
—on an office building door

**WARNING
THIS SCHOOL
IS ALARMED**
ON THE FRONT DOOR
OF A SCHOOL

In a laundrette:
Those using automatic washers should remove their clothes when the lights go out.

ALL DRINKING WATER IN THIS ESTABLISHMENT HAS BEEN PERSONALLY PASSED BY THE MANAGEMENT.
—sign in a café

A ROAD SIGN NEXT TO A RIVER:
WHEN THIS SIGN IS UNDER WATER THE ROAD IS IMPASSABLE.

Sign on an electricity pylon:
DANGER!
To touch these wires will cause instant death. Anyone found doing so will be prosecuted.

Notice outside public bar:
OUR PUBLIC BAR IS PRESENTLY NOT OPEN BECAUSE IT IS CLOSED.

After a recipe in
a cookery book:
WARNING
—If doubling the ingredients
you will make twice as many.

Automated announcement in a train:
**Please do not forget anything that
you take with you.**

In a first aid manual:
IF A PERSON FAINTS WHEN HE
IS STANDING UP HE COLLAPSES
TO THE GROUND.

REALLY ODD RELATIVES

My Auntie Dot
My Auntie Dot's a coffee pot.
She sits on the kitchen shelf,
Waiting for someone to take her down,
Muttering to herself.

'To be a coffee pot's my lot,'
She says. 'It's rather boring.
There's nothing to do, while I sit here,
I can't even practise pouring.

'A coffee pot is not what
I'd be if I could choose.
My sister's son has far more fun,
'Cause he's a pair of shoes!'

Par for the Course
When Auntie Fay began to neigh
And spend the day just eating hay,
My uncle said, 'It's par for the course.
Your auntie has become a horse.
I'll have to put her in the stable,
In the stall next to your Auntie Mabel!'

Relatively Speaking
What do you call a mother who is not very tall?
A minimum

Tracy Lacey's Family—A Generation Game
Willie Dilley married Dilys Willis.
Willie and Dilys Willis had three children—Billy
  Dilley, Millie Dilley and Lily Dilley.
Billy Dilley married Tilly Lilley.
Billy and Tilly Dilley had a daughter Gilly Dilley.
Gilly Dilley married Wally Colley.
Gilly and Wally Colley had four daughters—Holly
  Colley, Polly Colley, Mollie Colley and Dolly Colley.
Holly Colley married Fred Stead and had two
  children—Ed Stead and Jed Stead.
Polly Colley married Maurice Norris and had
  three children—Horace Norris, Doris Norris
  and Boris Norris.
Mollie Colley married Mick Crick and had
  two children—Dick Crick and Nick Crick.
Dolly Colley married Casey Lacey and had one
  child Tracy Lacey.

1. Who was Tracy Lacey's grandmother?

2. How many cousins does Tracy Lacey have?

3. What relation is Willie Dilley to Tracy Lacey?

Uncle Frank

When we're all asleep in bed,
My Uncle Frank unscrews his head.
He fixes on another one
And sets off for a night of fun.

It really gave me quite a jolt,
The first time that I saw the bolt,
Which Uncle proudly showed to me
In the cellar after tea.

He says the reason for his fame
Is that we share a famous name:
Oh, I forgot to tell you mine,
Our family's name is Frankenstein.

PICKLED BUG AND LAMBO

I Wish I Was a Little Grub

I wish I was a little grub
With whiskers round my tummy.
I'd climb into a honey-pot
And make my tummy gummy.
And then I'd crawl all over you
And make your tummy gummy, too.

What were the only animals not to go
into the ark in pairs?
Maggots. They went in an apple.

What should you do if two snails are having a fight?
Leave them to slug it out.

What do snails use to keep their shells shiny?
Snail varnish.

The Baby Glow-worm

The baby glow-worm was feeling glum,
He wasn't a happy chappie.
His mother had covered up his light
By putting on his nappy.

Bug in a Jug

Curious fly,
Vinegar jug,
Slippery edge,
Pickled bug.

Sheepish Questions

What do sheep enjoy on a hot summer's day?
A *baa-baa-cue.*

What do you call a sheep which has had a
makeover?
A *new ewe.*

What do you call a sheep with a machine gun?
Lambo.

What do you call a sheep thief?
A *ram raider.*

What do sheep write at the end of their letters?
Ewes sincerely.

Where does a sheep go to get a haircut?
The baa baas.

What do you get if you cross a sheep with a kangaroo?
A woolly jumper.

Why didn't the lamb volunteer to be in the school show?
Because it felt sheepish about taking part.

How do sheep keep warm in winter?
Central bleating.

What do lady sheep call their coats?
Ewe-niforms

HILARIOUS HISTORY

At which battle were the English army flushed
with success after defeating the French?
Waterloo.

What was the Emperor of France called after
he was hit by a cannonball?
Napoleon Blownapart

How do we know Rome was built at night?
Everyone says Rome wasn't built in a day.

Where was the Magna Carta signed?
At the bottom.

How did Vikings send secret messages?
By Norse code.

Why Elizabeth I Never Married
She couldn't find a suitor to suit her
Among all her courtiers at court.
As she smoothed down her dress,
She said, 'Well, I guess,
I'm just not the marrying sort.'

SHIVER ME TIMBERS!

Customer: Have you got a DVD of
Pirates of the Caribbean?
Shop assistant: We don't sell pirate DVDs.

Why did the pirate put a coat of paint on his ship?
Because its timbers were shivering.

Why did the pirate cross the road?
To get to the second-hand shop.

Why was the pirate, who was shipwrecked on the desert island, never hungry?
Because of all the sand which is there.

How much did the pirate have to pay for his hook and his wooden leg?
An arm and a leg.

How do you make a pirate angry?
Take away the p and he becomes irate.

DID YOU HEAR ABOUT...?

Did you hear about the fool who goes around
saying 'No' all the time?
No.
Oh, so it's you!

Did you hear about the really intelligent horse?
He was outstanding in his field.

Did you hear about the schoolgirl who couldn't
get to grips with decimals?
She couldn't see the point.

Did you hear about my friend Sid?
He was the victim of ID theft. Now he's just called S.

Did you hear about the stupid Australian who got
a new boomerang for his birthday?
He spent two days trying to throw the old one away.

Did you hear about the absent-minded hotel
guest who went round and round in a revolving
door for three hours?
He didn't know whether he was coming or going.

Did you hear about the monster who had eight arms?
He said they came in handy.

Did you hear about the carpenter's son?
He's a chip off the old block.

Answers to riddles and puzzles

Seaside Riddles
1: sand; 2: pier; 3: tide; 4: lighthouse; 5: sandcastle;
6: windsurf; 7: anchor; 8: crab; 9: waves; 10:
mermaid.

Name the Girl, Name the Boy
1: Cathy; 2: Craig; 3: Tabitha; 4: Andrew; 5: Bertha; 6:
Bella; 7: Rodney; 8: Daniel; 9: Glenda; 10: Piers.

Tracy Lacey's Family—A Generation Game
1: Gilly Dilley; 2: seven; 3: Great-great-grandfather.

ACKNOWLEDGEMENTS

This collection Copyright © John Foster 2012
The following poems are copyright © John Foster 2012 and may not be
reproduced without permission:

'A Cheeky Boy Called Robert Rung'
'Advice To Travellers'
'Charlotte Cul-de-Sac'
'Dine At Dracula's'
'Epitaph for a Football Referee'
'Ernie—A Cautionary Tale'
'Fantasy Football'
'Get Ratty'
'Hark! The Herald Angels Sing'
'Holiday Hints'
'I Know a Girl Called Norah Bone'
'Monday's Child Is As Slimy As a Snail'
'Mr Wister's Sister'
'My Auntie Dot'
'Nicola Nicholas'
'Nursery Rhyme Storytapes'
'Par For the Course'
'People Who Lived Up To Their Names'
'Sandra Slater'
'School Reports—Ann'
'Seaside Riddles'
'Shaun Short's Short Shorts'
'Six Sick Sikhs Met Six Sick Sheiks'
'Sue Shore Shrieked'
'Ride-a-sock horse'
'Ten Shakespeare Plays You Won't Have Seen'
'The Goalkeeper from Tibet'
'The Magician's Ghost'
'Uncle Frank'
'Underwood's Underwear'
'Who's That at the Door?'
'Why Elizabeth I Never Married'
'You Can Count On Me'